KT-569-204

This book belongs to

....

Mermaid School

by Alexandra Robinson

make
believe
ideas

Get the most from this reader

• •

Before reading:

Look at the pictures and discuss them together. Ask questions such as, "What do we call this sea creature?"

Relate the topic to your child's world. For example, say: "What would you like to bake in cooking class?"

● Familiarise your child with book vocabulary by using terms such as *word, letter, title, author* and *text*.

• •

During reading:

Prompt your child to sound out unknown words. Draw attention to neglected middle or end sounds.

Encourage your child to use the pictures as clues to unknown words.

● Occasionally ask what might happen next, and then check together as you read on.

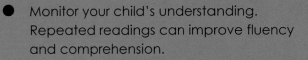

- Monitor your child's understanding. Repeated readings can improve fluency and comprehension.

- Keep reading sessions short and enjoyable. Stop if your child becomes tired or frustrated.

• •

After reading:

- Discuss the book. Encourage your child to form opinions with questions such as, "What did you like best about this book?"

- Help your child work through the fun activities at the back of the book. Then ask him or her to reread the story. Praise any improvement.

8

The mermaids
swim to school.

Mermaid School

First, they have music class with Miss Jellyfish.

11

Then, they have art class with Mrs Narwhal.

Next, they have cooking class with Mr Snail.

14

15

Later, they have writing class with Miss Crab.

Last, they have football class with Mr Whale.

But they find it hard to kick the ball!

1. Who teaches the music class?

2. Why do the mermaids find it hard to kick the ball?

3. Would you like to go to this school? Why?

22

Sight Words

Learning sight words helps you read fluently. Practise these sight words from the book. Use them in sentences of your own.

but

they

then

have

it

with

the

to

♋ Rhyming Words ♋

Can you find the rhyming pairs?
Say them aloud.

to

kick

swim

him

do

pick

Read the words, and then trace them with your finger.

ball

have

class

swim

first

music

ঌ Silly Sentences ঌ

Have fun filling in the gap in each
sentence. Use the ideas below
or make up your own.

The mermaids swim to ....

They have .... class
with Mrs Fish.